_____

Grandpa's Full Name

_____   _____

Date of Birth   Place of Birth

_____

Grandpa's Mother's Full Name

_____   _____

Date of Birth   Place of Birth

_____

Grandpa's Father's Full Name

_____   _____

Date of Birth   Place of Birth

Grandpa

His stories. His words.

COMPENDIUM™
INCORPORATED

live inspired.

WITH SPECIAL THANKS TO

Jason Aldrich, Gerry Baird, Jay Baird, Neil Beaton, Josie Bissett, Laura Boro, Melissa Carlson, Tiffany Parente Connors, Jim & Alyssa Darragh & Family, Rob Estes, Pamela Farrington, Michael & Leianne Flynn & Family, Sarah Forster, Michael J. Hedge, Liz Heinlein & Family, Renee & Brad Holmes, Jennifer Hurwitz, Heidi Jones, Sheila Kamuda, Michelle Kim, Carol Anne Kennedy, June Martin, David Miller, Carin Moore, Jessica Phoenix and Tom DesLongchamp, Janet Potter & Family, Joanna Price, Heidi & Jose Rodriguez, Diane Roger, Alie Satterlee, Sam T. Schick, Kirsten & Garrett Sessions, Andrea Summers, Brien Thompson, Helen Tsao, Anne Whiting, Kobi & Heidi Yamada & Family, Justi and Tote Yamada & Family, Bob and Val Yamada, Kaz & Kristin Yamada & Family, Tai & Joy Yamada, Anne Zadra, August & Arline Zadra, Dan Zadra, and Gus & Rosie Zadra.

CREDITS

Compiled by Dan Zadra
Designed by Steve Potter
Created by Kobi Yamada

ISBN: 978-1-935414-05-6

Printed in China

Dear Grandpa...

In your hands, you hold one of the most thoughtful gifts you could ever give your family. It won't take long for you to respond to the questions in this little book, but future generations will treasure your answers forever.

Imagine if your grandfather had been able to tuck away a similar book for you. What a joy to discover a few of his favorite memories of the old days, in his own handwriting. Well, now is your chance to pick up a pen and create a wonderful family heirloom of your own.

Like a trip down memory lane, the following pages will whisk you back to another time and place. The questions are simple and straightforward, but only you can provide the answers—and that's what makes this book so special.

When you were a child, what did you want to be when you grew up? What was your old neighborhood like? Who were your best friends? Have fun with your answers—they don't need to be formal or complicated. Just answer straight from the heart, and the result is sure to be magical to those who love you.

Grandpa, do you remember hearing any stories about why and how your ancestors came to this country?

_____

_____

_____

_____

_____

_____

_____

_____

_____

_____

Grandpa, did you get to know your own grandfather and grandmother? What did they look like, and what were some of their best qualities?

_____

_____

_____

_____

_____

_____

_____

_____

_____

Grandpa, can you tell a story about your mom — something that reflects her personality or values?

_____

_____

_____

_____

_____

_____

_____

_____

Grandpa, can you tell a story about your dad—something that reflects his personality or values?

_____

_____

_____

_____

_____

_____

_____

_____

Grandpa, did you, your parents, or your grandparents live through any wars? Which ones—and how did they affect you?

_____

_____

_____

_____

_____

_____

_____

_____

_____

Grandpa, what were the costs of everyday things such as food, cars, gas, and movies when you were growing up?

_____

_____

_____

_____

_____

_____

_____

_____

Grandpa, describe your childhood home. Can you picture the kitchen? Your bedroom? The living room? The yard?

_____

_____

_____

_____

_____

_____

_____

_____

Grandpa, how far away were your grade school and high school — and how did you get there each day?

_____

_____

_____

_____

_____

_____

_____

_____

Grandpa, when you were a boy, was your family always able to make ends meet? When times were tough, in what ways did you have to tighten your belts or do without?

_____

_____

_____

_____

_____

_____

_____

_____

Grandpa, what was your first car? Were you a safe driver?

_____

_____

_____

_____

_____

_____

_____

_____

_____

Grandpa, who did you pick for president when you were first able to vote, and did he do a good job?

_____

_____

_____

_____

_____

_____

_____

_____

_____

Grandpa, what were some of your favorite hobbies, sports or pastimes when you were a child?

_____

_____

_____

_____

_____

_____

_____

_____

_____

Grandpa, when you were a boy, how much did you have to help with the family chores, and what were they?

_____

_____

_____

_____

_____

_____

_____

_____

Grandpa, why did your parents give you your name? Did you have a nickname in grade school or high school? If so, how and why did you get it?

_____

_____

_____

_____

_____

_____

_____

_____

_____

Grandpa, what kind of social crowd did you hang out with in high school? Were you more of an athlete, an honor student, a rebel?

_____

_____

_____

_____

_____

_____

_____

_____

Grandpa, was your mother or father a good cook? Growing up, what were your favorite family meals or recipes?

_____

_____

_____

_____

_____

_____

_____

_____

_____

Grandpa, when you were a boy, what was your favorite holiday, and how did your family celebrate it?

_____

_____

_____

_____

_____

_____

_____

_____

_____

_____

Grandpa, what was your first job, how much were you paid, and did you like it?

_____

_____

_____

_____

_____

_____

_____

_____

_____

Grandpa, how old were you when you first moved out of your parents' house? How did you feel, and what was your first place like?

_____

_____

_____

_____

_____

_____

_____

_____

Grandpa, can you tell a story or two about any black sheep or colorful characters in the family?

_____

_____

_____

_____

_____

_____

_____

_____

_____

Grandpa, are there any family heirlooms or historic objects (a Civil War uniform, a trunk that went through Ellis Island, etc.) that have been handed down from generation to generation — and where are they now?

_____

_____

_____

_____

_____

_____

_____

_____

Grandpa, what were two major news events of your life? How did you feel about them? What influence did they have on you?

_____

_____

_____

_____

_____

_____

_____

_____

_____

Grandpa, how did you meet Grandma, where did you get married, and where did you go on your honeymoon?

_____

_____

_____

_____

_____

_____

_____

_____

Grandpa, what was it like to start a family?

_____

_____

_____

_____

_____

_____

_____

_____

_____

_____

Grandpa, when you were raising your kids, what were your most memorable family vacations or events?

_____

_____

_____

_____

_____

_____

_____

_____

_____

_____

Grandpa, everyone experiences disappointments in life — things they wish would have turned out differently. What have been some of yours?

_____

_____

_____

_____

_____

_____

_____

_____

_____

Grandpa, what have been three or four of the happiest or most satisfying times of your life so far?

_____

_____

_____

_____

_____

_____

_____

_____

_____

Grandpa, who were some people you looked up to when you were growing up — and who do you look up to now?

_____

_____

_____

_____

_____

_____

_____

_____

_____

Grandpa, in what ways has the world changed for the better (and for the worse) since you were a kid?

_____

_____

_____

_____

_____

_____

_____

_____

_____

Grandpa, what do you miss most about the old days?

_____

_____

_____

_____

_____

_____

_____

_____

_____

Grandpa, what makes you optimistic (or pessimistic) about today's younger generation?

_____

_____

_____

_____

_____

_____

_____

_____

_____

Grandpa, in what ways do you think you have become "wiser" as you've grown older?

_____

_____

_____

_____

_____

_____

_____

_____

_____

Grandpa, what's an important lesson your parents taught you — something you've tried to live by and share with your own kids?

_____

_____

_____

_____

_____

_____

_____

_____

_____

Grandpa, what are some of the best things in life that money can't buy?

_____

_____

_____

_____

_____

_____

_____

_____

_____

Grandpa, what are the best (or most fun) things about being a grandparent?

_____

_____

_____

_____

_____

_____

_____

_____

Grandpa, how would you finish this sentence: The secret to staying young is to...

_____

_____

_____

_____

_____

_____

_____

_____

_____

Grandpa, what's next for you? What are some of your goals and plans for the next chapter of your life?

_____

_____

_____

_____

_____

_____

_____

_____

_____

Grandpa, has life been good to you? What are some of the things you are most grateful for?

_____

_____

_____

_____

_____

_____

_____

_____

_____

Memories are
our greatest
inheritance.

—PETER HAMILL